The Cellar

Brandon Robsha

Published in association with
The Basic Skills Agency

Hodder & Stoughton

Acknowledgements
Illustrations: Jim Eldridge
Cover: Mathew Williams/The Organisation

Orders: please contact Bookpoint Ltd, 39 Milton Park, Abingdon, Oxon OX14
4TD. Telephone: (44) 01235 400414, Fax: (44) 01235 400454. Lines are open
from 9.00–6.00, Monday to Saturday, with a 24 hour message answering service.
Email address: orders@bookpoint.co.uk

British Library Cataloguing in Publication Data
A catalogue record for this title is available from The British Library

ISBN 0 340 74235 6

First published 1999
Impression number   10 9 8 7 6 5 4 3 2 1
Year   2004 2003 2002 2001 2000 1999

Copyright © 1999 Brandon Robshaw

Typeset by Fakenham Photosetting Ltd, Fakenham, Norfolk.
Printed in Great Britain for Hodder & Stoughton Educational, a division of
Hodder Headline Plc, 338 Euston Road, London NW1 3BH by Athenaeum Press,
Gateshead.

The Cellar

Contents

1

No Money!

The letter-box opened.
Three bills fell on the mat.
Mark bent down and picked them up.

They all said the same thing,
in great big red letters –
FINAL DEMAND.

'Great,' said Mark to himself. 'Just great.'
He had to pay these bills soon or his gas,
phone and electricity would be cut off.

But he had no money to pay the bills.
The rent was due, too.
And if he didn't pay that,
he would be out on the streets.

Where could he get some money?
He had no relatives to borrow from.
He had friends.
But he already owed them money.
Anyway, he needed hundreds of pounds.
His friends didn't have that kind of money.
Maybe he should get a job.
But Mark didn't really want a job.
He didn't want to get up early every morning.
He was young and he wanted to have fun.

Mark screwed up the bills
and threw them on the table.
He looked out of the window
and decided to go out.
He couldn't worry about money
on a beautiful day like this.
Something would turn up.

2

Too Good
to be True

Mark walked through the park.
The flowers were all in bloom.
Mark started to feel happy.

Something will turn up, he said to himself.
Maybe I'll find a lottery ticket
and win the jackpot.
But then he smiled to himself.
Who am I kidding, he thought.
Things like that don't happen in real life.

Mark began to feel thirsty.

He needed a drink.

Just outside the park

was a small newsagent's shop.

Mark went in and bought a can of drink.

On his way out, he looked at the adverts
in the window.

One of them caught his eye.

'DO YOU WANT FIFTY THOUSAND
POUNDS?' it said.

'ARE YOU A YOUNG, GOOD-LOOKING
MAN UNDER 25?

THEN CALL AT 16 OXFORD GARDENS.
YOU COULD EARN FIFTY THOUSAND
POUNDS!'

Mark was under 25.

In fact, he was only 20.

And he was good-looking.

At least, he thought so.

The advert seemed too good to be true.

He read it again.

'DO YOU WANT FIFTY THOUSAND POUNDS?'
Yes, he did.
He did want fifty thousand pounds.

He began to laugh.
It was like a dream come true.

Oxford Gardens was not far away.
Mark decided to go there at once.

3

Helen's Offer

Oxford Gardens was a big, smart road
full of big, smart houses.
Number 16 was one of the biggest
and smartest of all.
Six stone steps led up to the front door.
Mark went up the steps and rang the bell.

The door opened.
A tall, thin woman stood there.
She looked about 50 years old.
She had long black hair.

'Yes?'

'I've come about the advert,' said Mark.

'Good,' said the woman. 'You'll do nicely.

Very nicely.'

She gave a little smile.

There was something funny about her teeth.

'What's your name?' she asked.

'Mark.'

'Come in, then, Mark.

My name is Helen, by the way.'

Mark followed her down the hall

into a great big room.

'Take a seat,' said Helen.

Mark sat down.

'About the fifty thousand pounds . . . ' he said.

'Good!' said Helen.

'I like a man who gets straight to the point!'

'What do I have to do to get the money?'

'What do you have to do?' said Helen.

'That's simple.

You have to marry me.'

She gave Mark a great big smile.
And now, he could see
what was wrong with her teeth.

They were pointed.

4

Mark's Decision

'You look shocked,' said Helen.
'Would you like a cup of tea?'
'No thanks,' said Mark. 'I have to go now.'
'I make very nice tea.'
'I'm sure you do,' said Mark,
'but I have to go now.'

He stood up.
'What's the matter?' asked Helen.
'Don't you want to marry me?'
'I don't even know you,' said Mark.

'But you could get to know me,' said Helen,
smiling at him with her pointed teeth.

Mark walked out of the room.
Helen followed him into the hall.
'If you change your mind . . .' she said,
'I'll be waiting for you.
And so will the fifty thousand pounds.'
She opened the front door
and waved as he walked away.

Mark could not stop thinking
about Helen's strange offer.
She must be mad.
You couldn't just buy people
as if they were things in a shop.

All the same, it wasn't every day
he turned down fifty thousand pounds.
It made him feel a bit strange.

He got home and opened the door
of his bedsit.

The bills were lying on the table
where he had left them.
FINAL DEMAND,
they said in big red letters.

Of course he was right
to turn down Helen's offer.
Wasn't he?

5

Return to Oxford Gardens

Over the next few days
Mark tried to put the fifty thousand pounds
out of his mind.
But it was not easy.

One evening, Mark felt like going out again.
He picked up the phone to call his friends.
But there was no sound.
The line was dead.
So that was that. The phone had been cut off.

Mark went into the kitchen.

He decided to cook himself a fried egg.

That would cheer him up.

He switched on the cooker.

Nothing happened.

So that was that. The gas had been cut off.

And then the lights went out.

So that was that. The electricity had been cut off.

There was a knock at the door.

Mark went to open it.

The landlord was standing there.

'I want the rent,' he said.

'You still owe me for last month.

Have you got it?'

'Not today, but . . .' began Mark.

'I'm coming back tomorrow,' said the landlord.

'And if you can't pay, you're out, mate.

Out on the streets!'

Mark closed the door and sat down.

He thought for a long time.

Then he got up and put his coat on.
He went straight round to Oxford Gardens.
He climbed the six stone steps
and knocked on the door.
It opened at once.
Helen was standing there, smiling.
Her pointed teeth glinted.

'I knew you'd come back, darling,' she said.

6

The Plan

They were married six weeks later.
Mark didn't like Helen much. Or her teeth.
But he wasn't going to let her teeth
stand between him and fifty thousand pounds.

Anyway, he had had an idea.
Once she gave him the fifty grand,
he could run away and leave her, couldn't he?
What was to stop him?

He found out as soon as the wedding was over.
Helen opened an account for him
with fifty thousand pounds in.
But the account had a limit
on how much he could take out.
He could only take out fifty pounds a day.

'Why can't I take it all out?' asked Mark.
'Fifty pounds a day isn't much.'
'If you took it all out,
you might run away and leave me.'
'Oh, I'd never do that!' said Mark.
'Better safe than sorry, darling,' said Helen.

They went to Paris for their honeymoon.
Helen bought Mark lots of presents –
new clothes, new shoes
and a gold cigarette lighter.
It wasn't too bad, being married, thought Mark.
He didn't really fancy Helen.
She was too old, for one thing.
But she was all right
if you didn't look at her teeth.

Anyway, thought Mark, he now had the money
to go out and meet girls.
That would cheer him up.

After the honeymoon,
Helen had to go back to work in the City.
'You don't mind being on your own
in the daytime, do you?' she asked Mark.
'You can have a nice rest.'
'That's fine,' said Mark. He liked resting.
'You can go in any room in the house
when I'm not here,' said Helen,
'EXCEPT the cellar.'
'Why not the cellar?' asked Mark.
'Don't ask why. Just NEVER,
EVER try to go in there.
Do you understand?'
'Of course I understand,' said Mark.

He looked at the cellar door.
He wondered what was down there.

7

Inside the Cellar

Mark found living with Helen very comfortable.
The food was good.
He liked having money in his pocket.

He wished that Helen would let him go out more.
She didn't like him seeing his friends.

But at least he was free to laze about.
Helen never asked him to do any work
about the house.

During the day, when she was out,
he had nothing to do.
Nothing to do but
wonder what was behind the cellar door.

Mark looked at that door 20 times a day.
What could be behind it?
He tried the handle a few times.
But it was always locked.

And then, one day, Mark saw
that the key was left in the lock.
Mark remembered what Helen had said.
'NEVER, EVER try to go in there.'
But if he went in there now,
how would she know?

He turned the key and pushed open the door.
Inside, it was very dark and very cold.
Mark couldn't find the light switch.
He took out his gold lighter
and flicked it on.

He saw a flight of steps leading down.
He went down the steps.
The lighter cast strange shadows
on the walls.

He reached the bottom of the steps.
It was even colder down here.
All around the room were deep freezers.
Mark lifted up the lid of one.
And then froze with horror
at the sight that met his eyes.

Inside the freezer
was the naked body of a man.
It was covered in red tooth-marks.
The kind of marks
that pointed teeth would make.

Mark lifted up the lid
of another freezer.
He saw the same thing.
Another naked body.
More red tooth-marks.

Mark was so shocked and scared
that he dropped his lighter.
He was left in darkness.

He felt around the floor,
looking for the lighter.
He couldn't find it.

He was in a cold sweat.
He had to get out of here.
He had to get out of this horrible cellar.

It was so dark
that he couldn't even see the stairs.
He felt around until he touched them.
Thank God, he said to himself.

And then he heard the sound
of the front door opening.

Helen was home.

8

Caught!

Mark had never run so fast in his life.
He was up the stairs in under a second.
He reached the hall just before
Helen came in through the front door.
'Hello Helen!' he said.
He was panting for breath.
Helen looked at him.
'Why are you so out of breath?'
'I was in the kitchen,' said Mark.
'I ran out as fast as I could when I heard you.
I was so happy that you were back!'

Helen looked pleased.

'You're a good boy,' she said.

'Now you can run back in the kitchen
and put the kettle on.

Let's have some tea.

I'll be with you in a minute.'

Mark went into the kitchen.

He shut the door behind him.

He took deep breaths.

He was safe – for the time being.

But it wasn't safe to stay here.

He had to get out and tell the police.

Maybe he should make a run for it.

But was there time?

Helen would be back any minute.

He didn't want her to catch him in the hall.

He would have to wait.

When she was asleep tonight, he'd leave.

He'd go straight to the police.

The kitchen door opened and Helen came in.
'Here, let me finish the tea, darling.'

She stood with her back to Mark
so that he could not quite see
what she was doing.
'Here you are, darling,' she said.

Mark drank some tea.
Be calm, he told himself.
She didn't know he'd been
down in the cellar.
He was safe – for the time being.
'I make nice tea, don't I?' said Helen.
'Oh yes,' said Mark.
In fact, the tea tasted a bit funny.
But he drank some more to please her.

He needed a cigarette.
He took one out and put it in his mouth.
He looked in his pocket for his lighter.
It wasn't there.

He looked in his other pocket.
It wasn't there either.

'Is this what you're looking for?' asked Helen.
She held up his gold cigarette lighter.
She was smiling.

9

The Punishment

Mark stared in horror.
He couldn't speak.

'I just went down to the cellar,' said Helen.
She was still smiling.
'I went to see my ex-husbands.
I like to keep in touch.
And guess what I found there?
Yes! This lighter!
Isn't that funny?
Can you explain it, darling?'

Mark tried to run for the door.
But his legs wouldn't move.
His body felt heavy.
He sat down in a chair.

'The tea...' he managed to say.
'Yes, the tea. Drugged, of course,' said Helen.
'I didn't want to do this to you.
I liked you, Mark.
I thought we might stay together
for a good long time.
But you went down in the cellar, didn't you?
They always do in the end.
So now you'll have to go and join them.'

She came towards Mark.
Her mouth opened wide.
Mark tried to get up, but he couldn't move.

The last thing he saw
was her pointed teeth,
glinting,
coming closer and closer.